New Original Drama Series

SUN 10/9C | JULY 11

INTRODUCTION

Jim Longworth is an attractive and brilliant Chicago homicide detective with a reputation for being difficult. When his captain wrongfully accuses him of sleeping with his wife and shoots him, he is exiled and forced to relocate. He lands in the sleepy, middle-of-nowhere town of Palm Glade, outside of Florida's Everglades, where sunshine and golf are plentiful and crime is seemingly at a minimum. But Longworth soon finds out this town isn't quite as idyllic as he originally thought, when murders keep piling up. Each case pulls Longworth off the golf course and reluctantly into his element as one of the sharpest homicide detectives to wear a badge.

Between practicing his short game, trying to get a date with Callie - a quick-witted, beautiful medical student with a twelve-year-old son and a husband in prison - and trying to solve countless homicide cases, Longworth's transition to his new surroundings is a bit more difficult than expected. He realizes the skies in this new town are sunny with a chance of homicide.

"PILOT"

WRITTEN BY

CLIFTON CAMPBELL

THE GLADES

Executive Producer.......GARY RANDALL

Executive Producer.......CLIFTON CAMPBELL

Co-Executive Producer....LORI-ETTA TAUB

Director................PETER O'FALLON

CAST

Jim Longworth...........MATT PASSMORE

Callie Cargill..........KIELE SANCHEZ

Carlos Sanchez..........CARLOS GOMEZ

Jeff Cargill............URIAH SHELTON

Daniel Green............JORDAN WALL

Erin Williams...........ABBY PIVARONAS

Mike Ogletree...........JOHN CARROLL LYNCH

Justin Brussard.........MICHAEL SEAN ROARK

ACT ONE

FADE IN:

EXT. PALM GLADE STATE PRESERVE - MORNING

A blast of sky and sun. The wet smell of
brine lays a heavy canopy over three-
hundred year old mangroves. A place where
lush green earth meets clear blue sky.

A wave of humid air pushes Spanish moss
out over Fisheating Creek, a dark, handsome
river that cuts through Palm Glade,
Florida. One of many Pinkberry communities
that sprung up east of Tampa in the last
half-decade, thanks to cheap mortgages and
really bad ideas. We know how that worked
out.

CREDITS over its indigenous beauty; a
virtual Garden of Eden, a million years
old and still in the game. Caladium the
size of an elephant's ear anchor a line of
flowering plants, herbaceous fern and fleshy
white magnolia. Peach palm sagos, entwined
in passion vine. A leggy Blue Heron picks
at the mud bank. A couple of small gators
drift silently among the lilies, little
more than a pair of eyes, keeping an eye
on everything. Such as

A RED SUV

Parked thirty feet from the creek. Von
Dutch detailing, 20 inch rims, suggesting
an owner of a certain age.

INT. RED SUV - MORNING

Inside, a man and a girl, asleep. Not
cuddling, hardly even touching. Oh, and
the girl - she's not wearing pants. Just

an oversized man's jersey riding up high enough to see a pair of pink and blue striped panties. From GAP, if I had to guess.

The man, JUSTIN, is a good looking kid of 22, with an athletic build. The girl, ERIN, is 16. Soft blonde hair, a hard and tight body. Two kids from middle-class families, exploring the nature of things. Both dead asleep...

Until one of those heron leap off the bank with a shrieking whoop, and glides, whooping, out over the swamp.

Waking Justin. His eyes open and we know immediately this kid did some drinking last night. Red, bleary eyes. Head pounding. He struggles for short term memory, looks over at Erin, dead asleep, vintage tee and panties - jogging some of last night back to him. He fishes around a dashboard cluttered with beer cans for his smokes. She stirs but does not wake.

Justin studies her body. More of the night returns to him in a flood of drunken memories, driving his need for fresh air.

EXT. FISHEATING CREEK - MORNING

Justin steps out, shirtless, barefoot. He scratches at his face, rolls the kinks out of his neck and shoulders.

Heads for the creek over cypress root that knob like veins along the ground.

He drops to his knees at the creek, running water over his face and through his hair. Shakes out a smoke, which he lights and inhales, deeply. He turns to look back at the SUV, to see that the girl has not moved. The cigarette is making him sicker, so he flicks it into the creek, the butt dying in the black water with a tssssst, not far from a body. A dead one.

A MIDDLE AGED WOMAN

Without a head, hands or feet, lies in the shallow mud. The better part of her right leg and shoulder bitten clean off.

JUSTIN

Stares at the body for a long beat. Trying to focus. He struggles through the knee-deep water to get a closer look, stopping a few yards away. The closer look sends him stumbling back for shore, where he collapses on the bank to get sick.

INT. RED SUV - MORNING

Erin wakes to the sound of his RETCHING. She sits up, sees Justin at the edge of the creek -- events of the night quickly returning to her, but a different night from the clarity in her eyes, causing her to reach for something around her neck - a locket that apparently is missing.

Her eyes dart around the car's interior, looking for, then finding the LOCKET on the floor. She grabs it, opens it up --

Whoever's photo is inside, giving her pause. She stares at it with sad purpose. Then closes it, looping it around her neck as she fumbles around the dash of the car for her watch, checking the time.

                    ERIN
          Shit.

She stands on the horn.

                    ERIN
          Justin! Shit.

The HORN sends Justin into a second wave
of retching.

Off which, the camera CRANES up and over
the mangrove to FIND the tri-bay area of
Tampa/St. Pete/Clearwater, a mile and a
half west, buffeting the azure waters of
the Gulf of Mexico.

                    LONGWORTH (V.O.)
          Hi, you've reached Jim
          Longworth...

INT. FLORIDA HIGHWAY PATROL VEHICLE - DAY

MIKE OGLETREE listens to the outgoing
message on his cell as he throws his
vehicle into park, eyes fixed on something
through the windshield --

                    LONGWORTH (V.O.)
          I'm either out seeking justice -
          or trying to break eighty - leave
          me a message...

                    OGLETREE
          Damn it, Jim. Answer the phone...

Ogletree disconnects, getting out of the
car as he dials another number --

EXT. FDLE - PALM GLADE SUBSTATION - DAY

Stepping to the wall where "Okeechobee
Southerners are Sub-Human" has been spray-
painted, as the phone on the other end
begins to RING...

EXT. BELLEAIR COUNTRY CLUB - DAY

JIM LONGWORTH over a ball on the fourteenth
fairway as his playing partner CARLOS'
phone rings. He checks the ID --

                    CARLOS
          Now he's calling me.

                    LONGWORTH
          Don't answer it.

Carlos flips open his cell phone. INTERCUT
as necessary.

                    CARLOS
          Hello?

                    OGLETREE
          Carlos - is he with you...

                    CARLOS
          Yeah, yeah, he's right here.

Carlos hands the phone to Longworth.

                    LONGWORTH
          You must've heard. I'm four over
          at the turn...birdied three,
          seven and ten with a lip out at
          eleven...

                    OGLETREE
          Yeah that's great. Look, we got a
          situation...

                    LONGWORTH
        -- *yeah* we do. I'm four holes away
        from breaking eighty for the first
        time in my life.

                    OGLETREE
        A woman's body was found in
        Fisheating creek.

                    LONGWORTH
        Well she's not gonna be any deader
        an hour from now.

Ogletree staring at the graffiti on the
wall.

                    OGLETREE
        And this message - tag or whatever
        - has been popping up all over
        town. I think they might be
        connected.

                    LONGWORTH
        Who found the body?

                    OGLETREE
        Some underaged kid and her
        boyfriend. Fell asleep in the
        swamp last night...

                    LONGWORTH
        How underaged we talking?

                    OGLETREE
        I dunno, sixteen, seventeen.

                    LONGWORTH
        What was she doing; was she doin'
        the guy?

                    OGLETREE
          I didn't ask her that.

                    LONGWORTH
          Well what the hell did you ask?

                    OGLETREE
          Nothing, I'm still trying to find
          her parents...

                    LONGWORTH
          Listen, just stick her in a room
          and don't let her talk to anyone.
          I want a clean shot at her before
          her parents shut her up.

                    OGLETREE
          Jim...

Longworth hangs up. Ogletree, frustrated,
annoyed, as he disconnects and lumbers
inside the Sub-Station.

                    LONGWORTH
          Call your wife and open your
          office.

                    CARLOS
          It's Sunday; my office is closed.

                    LONGWORTH
          I just opened it.

Longworth waves a HISPANIC GROUNDSKEEPER
over.

                    LONGWORTH
          Excuse me. See this ball? Es yo
          bolito - si?

The groundskeeper nods as Longworth flashes his badge.

> LONGWORTH
> This ball is part of a murder investigation. Anybody messes with my ball and you go to jail? Comprende?

The worker nods. Longworth gets in the cart with Carlos and they ride off. The worker stands there.

> CUT TO:

INT. FLORIDA HIGHWAY PATROL - BREAK ROOM - DAY

Longworth waits for a burrito to reheat in the microwave. Ogletree stirs a packet of sugar into his coffee from Robbie's as he teases out details from a work in progress protocol.

> OGLETREE
> No scar tissue, no water in her lungs - nothing in her stomach...

The microwave DINGS. Longworth goes for his burrito.

> OGLETREE
> ...identity and Cause of Death inconclusive without the head -- you might wanna give that a --

> LONGWORTH
> Ah! Damn it.

Longworth burns his hand grabbing the hot burrito.

                    OGLETREE
You wanna go look at the body?

                    LONGWORTH
She's dead. I wanna talk to the
girl. Any word from her folks?

                    OGLETREE
Her mom is M.I.A. Apparently not
unusual for a weekend, especially
with her husband on a poker run in
the Keys.

                    LONGWORTH
Any o' these geniuses have a
record?

                    OGLETREE
Law abiding, far as we know.

                    LONGWORTH
What about the boy?

                    OGLETREE
Local kid. Justin Brussard.
Twenty-two...
         (beat)
I sent him home.

                    LONGWORTH
Why?

                    OGLETREE
He threw up on my keyboard giving
his statement.
         (beat)
Got a call in to the girl's folks.

Longworth heads off, Ogletree calling out
after him --

                    OGLETREE
          She's sixteen. Can't talk to her
          without a parent or guardian...

But Longworth is already on the move...

INT. FLORIDA HIGHWAY PATROL - CONFERENCE
ROOM - DAY

Longworth enters, sits across from Erin as
he eats his burrito. Introducing himself --

                    LONGWORTH
          Jim Longworth.

She looks at him.

                    ERIN
          You a cop?

                    LONGWORTH
               (nods)
          Lieutenant. You get anything to
          eat?
               (silence)
          You want something? Burrito or
          something? Something to drink?

She shakes her head no. Longworth looks at
her a beat.

                    LONGWORTH
          Would you be more comfortable if
          we waited till we located one of
          your parents?

                    ERIN
          My parents? Good luck with that.

LONGWORTH
You're okay talking to me, then?

She shrugs sure, whatever. Longworth sits
across from her.

LONGWORTH
We sent your whatever he is -
boyfriend or whatever, home. He
puked on my partner's keyboard.

ERIN
He drinks too much.

LONGWORTH
He's also older than you. Did you
guys have relations?

ERIN
What do you mean? Did I screw him?

LONGWORTH
Yeah, did you screw him.

ERIN
Is that important?

LONGWORTH
Maybe.

She looks at him a beat. Not sure where
he's going.

ERIN
I'm old enough to give consent.

LONGWORTH
You're sixteen. That's not old
enough. Legally.

                    ERIN
        Are you going to arrest him?

                  LONGWORTH
        Did he have sex with you?

                    ERIN
        No.
            (off his look)
        And what's this got to do with the
        woman without the head?

                  LONGWORTH
        I don't know yet.

Erin looks at him. Digesting that.

                  LONGWORTH
        He says you guys got out there a
        little after ten o'clock and slept
        out there all night? Did you see
        or hear anything?

                    ERIN
        You mean, related to the woman?

                  LONGWORTH
        Yeah. Did you see or hear anything
        that might help us identify who
        she was. Like the person or
        persons who dumped her there.

                    ERIN
        Maybe she died there.

                  LONGWORTH
        Maybe. But we don't think so.

                    ERIN
        What do you think happened?

LONGWORTH
I think she was killed somewhere
else and dumped there so an
alligator could destroy the
evidence.

Erin takes a beat with that. Shakes her
head no.

ERIN
I didn't hear anything.

LONGWORTH
What about this spot? Anything
about it special for you two?

ERIN
No.

LONGWORTH
No special meaning?

ERIN
No. Just a place to go.

LONGWORTH
A place other people go to maybe?
Young people. To party, get drunk.
Try sex?

She doesn't respond, but yeah, basically.

LONGWORTH
So it's kind of a dumb place to
dump a body. If someone knew that.

ERIN
Maybe it's a good place, if you're
tryin' to mess with the cops.

                    LONGWORTH
          Is that something you think about?
          Messing with us for trying to keep
          things safe and orderly?

                    ERIN
          I'm just saying.

                    LONGWORTH
          So was this your first time trying
          sex?

                    ERIN
          Trying?

                    LONGWORTH
          Hey, I'm still trying. Don't ever
          wanna get too good at a thing, it
          takes out all the magic.

                    ERIN
          How do you know she didn't float
          there from upriver?

                    LONGWORTH
          Doesn't figure that way,
          forensically.

                    ERIN
          Are you an expert in forensics?

                    LONGWORTH
          I'm an expert in all things
          homicidal, Erin. There isn't
          much about murder I don't know.
          Or can't find out. If I just keep
          asking the right questions.

They stare at each other.

CUT TO:

EXT. PALM GLADE STATE PRESERVE - FISHEATING
CREEK - AFTERNOON

Crime scene tape marks off a hundred or so
square feet which have been cordoned off
to the public. A State Police Department
vehicle sits inside the area, parked along
side the marsh.

We FIND Longworth, sitting on the bank,
shoes and socks off, rolling up his pant
legs. A 9-iron at his side, which he picks
up then wades into the water.

The water is to his mid-thigh. He tries to
peer down into the dark, brackish water as
he sifts through the silt with the 9-iron,
raking it across the river floor. He snags
on something, dips to fish around the bottom
with his hand, holding his head just above
the water line, when he suddenly lurches
out of the water, staggering back and out
of the way of

AN ANGRY FIVE FOOT ALLIGATOR
whipping in a near full-breech having
taken a good nip out of Longworth's hand.
Longworth stumbles back onto the bank, more
in shock than in pain as the alligator
drifts off, already losing interest in the
startled lawman.

CUT TO:

INT. TAMPA GRACE MEDICAL CENTER - EVENING

Longworth in a hospital gown, a bandage
over his right hand, is bent over an
exam table as a health care worker draws
antibiotic into a syringe behind him.

16

                    LONGWORTH
          Is this absolutely necessary?

The health care worker, CALLIE, a pretty
thirty-two year old with a tough veneer,
rubs an alcohol cotton ball on his ass.

                    CALLIE
          You want to die of infection?

                    LONGWORTH
          He looked pretty hygienic to me.

                    CALLIE
          Everyone looks hygienic till the
          blood work comes back.

She looks for a spot on his ass to
administer the shot, stops to run a finger
over scar tissue in the middle of his back.

                    CALLIE
          Either that's an exit wound or
          the surgeons in Chicago are all
          drunks.

He looks back at her, impressed she knew
what it was.

                    LONGWORTH
          My captain shot me.

                    CALLIE
          On purpose?

                    LONGWORTH
          He thought I was sleeping with his
          wife...

She sticks him with the needle, he blanches
slightly.

> LONGWORTH
>> -- I wasn't. But I was the only one in the department that wasn't.

She drops the gown to re-cover his ass. He holds up his bandaged hand, testing it, squeezing it open and closed.

> LONGWORTH
>> It feels like it's gonna hurt like hell later on.

> CALLIE
>> I can give you something for the pain, but a six pack of Heineken will do just as good. And if I do give you something and later on you want that Heineken...

Meaning, not on antibiotics, as he mimics a golf grip and swing, annoyed with the clunky bandage and wincing for the effort.

> LONGWORTH
>> Callie, is it?

She looks at him. He nods to her name tag -- how he knows this.

> LONGWORTH
>> How long you think I'm gonna have to wear this thing?

> CALLIE
>> You in some kind of hurry?

> LONGWORTH
>> I've got a Titleist with a perfect lie sitting on the fourteenth fairway at Belleair, waiting for

                    me to break eighty for the first
                    time in my life.

                              CALLIE
                    With that swing, I'm not
                    surprised.

She hands him a clipboard for his
signature.

                              CALLIE
                    Sign, date and initial where
                    indicated.

                              LONGWORTH
                    What am I signing?

                              CALLIE
                    You're releasing the medical
                    center from liability should
                    you lose that hand or die from
                    infection due to my incompetence.

                              LONGWORTH
                    I'm not signing that.

                              CALLIE
                    You will if you want your pants
                    back.

She leaves. He smiles, eyes trailing her
as she goes. Off which --

                                        FADE OUT:

                    END OF ACT ONE

ACT TWO

FADE IN:

INT. FLORIDA HIGHWAY PATROL - OFFICE - DAY

Ogletree, sitting uncomfortably at his desk over a file.

> LONGWORTH
> That thing helping?

He turns as Longworth steps up, nodding to the back support thing strapped to the back of Ogletree's chair.

> OGLETREE
> No. Lose your uniform again?

Ogletree in department khakis, Longworth in street clothes. An ongoing source of aggravation for Ogletree...

> LONGWORTH
> I'm just saying, hit the gym once in a while, every little thing wouldn't throw your back out.

> OGLETREE
> Yeah, we can be workout partners. Spend even more time together.
>   (re: the files)
> I got Missing Person files from Orlando, Ocala, Tampa, Miami. Nothing promising. I'm waiting for Jacksonville and Naples.

> LONGWORTH
> Naples? That's like old people. She wasn't that old.

                    OGLETREE
          Maybe she was visiting a relative.

                    LONGWORTH
          Dressed like that, I don't think
          so.

                    OGLETREE
          What's wrong with the way she was
          dressed?

                    LONGWORTH
          Someone she was visiting would've
          called it in if she went missing,
          don't you think?

Ogletree looks at him blankly.

                    LONGWORTH
          We may not have her head,
          compadre, but we still have ours.

Longworth heads off. Ogletree watches him
head out.

INT. FLORIDA DEPARTMENT OF LAW ENFORCEMENT –
LAB

Carlos over a microscope, Longworth poring
over a victim protocol.

                    CARLOS
          The club manager called. He's
          getting complaints that you've
          cordoned off an area around your
          ball on the fourteenth fairway.

                    LONGWORTH
          I want to finish the round.

                    CARLOS
It's going to be weeks before you
can swing a club. Go pick up your
ball.

                    LONGWORTH
I'm getting medical treatment,
I'll be fine by the end of the
week.
        (from the protocol)
Esophageal abrasions? What's that,
like heartburn? What would cause
that?

                    CARLOS
Acid reflux. Spicy food. You.

                    LONGWORTH
How spicy?

                    CARLOS
Spicy. Habanero spicy.

                    LONGWORTH
What's that test called again?

                    CARLOS
What test?

                    LONGWORTH
Barnucleous or something.

                    CARLOS
        (annoyed by the obvious)
A skin graft, to determine race.
She's white.

                    LONGWORTH
And tan. Any way to determine if

her tan was natural, or the result
of a tanning booth?

                    CARLOS
No. Both are caused from exposure
to UV rays...

                    LONGWORTH
Exposed evenly from a tanning bed
- or mottled, like a native?

Carlos looks up at him, annoyed but sees
his point.

                    CARLOS
          Fine. I'll do a barnucleous.

Carlos goes back to his eyepiece.

                    LONGWORTH
You know if she had any kids?

                    CARLOS
Pelvic density suggests not.

                    LONGWORTH
But you'll run a test to determine
anyway.
          (off his look)
If she's anything like my mom, she
and my sister talk five times a day
and they hate each other.

                    CARLOS
Whatever the hell that means.

                    LONGWORTH
It means I think it's time I found
a woman's perspective.

Carlos looks up from his eyepiece at that -- to see that he is gone.

INT. TAMPA GRACE MEDICAL CENTER - DAY

Longworth is having his wound re-dressed by a NURSE, when CALLIE walks by, bag over her shoulder, clearly on her way to the parking lot.

Longworth nods thanks to the nurse, hurries off to follow.

Falling in step with Callie as she hurries through the lobby.

                    LONGWORTH
          Hey. I was hoping I would catch you.

                    CALLIE
          Already not sure how I feel about
          that.

                    LONGWORTH
          I'd like to run something by you.

                    CALLIE
          Look, I just stopped by to pick up
          my check...

                    LONGWORTH
          See, I have this theory. Two
          theories, actually. I need someone
          like yourself to kind of walk it
          through with me.

                    CALLIE
          Don't you have co-workers for that
          kind of thing?

                    LONGWORTH
          I do, yeah, a *lot* of co-workers...

She stops at the automatic doors leading out
to the parking lot to fish out her keys --

                    LONGWORTH
          -- and a partner I guess, I mean,
          technically speaking. He heads up
          the local Highway Patrol. Nice
          enough guy, great wife. They
          have me over to dinner every
          Sunday. But he's not a very good
          cop. He's also not a health care
          professional. Or a woman. I need a
          woman's perspective.

                    CALLIE
          Who's a health care professional.

When a car HORN sounds, coming from a
KIA SORRENTO, parked under the entrance
overhang.

                    CALLIE
          Look, I really can't do this right
          now...

                    LONGWORTH
          The new Sorrento. Nice. Who's that
          waiting for you?

Meaning the BOY in the front seat, obviously
the horn honker.

                    CALLIE
          That's my husband.

                    LONGWORTH
          Your husband is twelve?

PHOTOGRAPHY FROM THE SET

Matt Passmore as Jim Longworth at **The Glades** photo shoot.

Kiele Sanchez as Callie Cargill visits Longworth's house.

Longworth hopes to break 80.

Longworth visits the crime scene.

Callie and Longworth share a beer.

Longworth shoots the gator as Daniel, a grad student in herpetology, looks on.

Wranglers pose their gator.

Longworth badges suspect, Justin.

Matt Passmore takes five to enjoy the view of the water between takes.

Longworth surveys the crime scene, of course with his putter.

Longworth with suspect, Erin.

Ogletree by his vehicle.

Lead Matt Passmore, Executive Producer Gary Randall,
and A&E Executive Scott Vila on the set.

Callie Cargill.

                    CALLIE
          Okay, he's my son.

                  LONGWORTH
          He looks annoyed.

                    CALLIE
          He's twelve.

                  LONGWORTH
          So there's a husband somewhere.

                    CALLIE
          Somewhere.

Vagueness, Longworth clocks, when her son
honks again.

                  LONGWORTH
          Then maybe a drink, later. Which
          sounds a lot like a date, but it's
          not.

                    CALLIE
          Later I have to feed my son and
          get on him about his homework.

                  LONGWORTH
          After that.

                    CALLIE
          After that I go to bed.

                  LONGWORTH
          Breakfast then, my treat, wherever
          you want.

She gives him a look, he smiles. Then the
horn again.

> CALLIE
> Okay, look. I'll feed my son and
> at least get him pretending to
> do his homework. You can stop by
> around eight, I'll give you thirty
> minutes.

> LONGWORTH
> Eight o'clock, thirty minutes,
> pretending to do his homework.

She gives him a look, grins despite herself
and heads off.

EXT. THE DON CESAR - BEACH RESORT - POOL
SIDE CABANA - DAY

A jewel of Deco renovation on the sugar-
white sand of St. Pete Beach.

Longworth talking to a man in a Blue
Blazer, who nods him off in a specific
direction, which Longworth follows.

He approaches Justin, wearing white shorts
and cotton shirt with epaulets, setting up
cabanas and guest umbrellas for the day.

> LONGWORTH
> Got a minute for some questions?

Justin glances up briefly. Continues to set
up chairs.

> JUSTIN
> Can't. Got to set up for the day.

> LONGWORTH
> Actually, now is what I meant.

Justin looks at Longworth, who's pulled
out his badge.

EXT. THE DON CESAR - BEACH - DAY

Justin sits with Longworth at the beach
side cafe. Parasails, turquoise water and
half-naked tourists in every direction.

                    JUSTIN
          I already gave that other guy my
          statement.

                    LONGWORTH
          Mixed in with chunks of whatever
          you had for dinner last night. I
          thought I'd do a little follow up
          now that you're, presumably, less
          hammered.

                    JUSTIN
          I didn't have anything to do with
          that lady getting killed.

                    LONGWORTH
          I don't know that.

                    JUSTIN
          Why would I tell you guys she was
          out there if I had something to do
          with it?

                    LONGWORTH
          I dunno, you're a moron? I already
          know you're not very bright...
                    (off his look)
          -- it's not murder, but rape will
          still get you eight years in
          prison, and you brought that to
          our attention.

                    JUSTIN
Rape? I didn't rape anybody.

                    LONGWORTH
The presumption is a sixteen-year-
old isn't emotionally ready to
consent to a sexual encounter,
so legally, the presumption is
a clear "no" across the board.
Having sex with someone who says
no, is rape.

                    JUSTIN
The legal age is sixteen. She
looked it up or something, went
online.

                    LONGWORTH
She lied to you about that. Which
I'm guessing you believed because
it synced up better with your
immediate needs. Any reason you
can think of why she lied to you
about that, like maybe it was her
first time?

                    JUSTIN
Her first time, that's hilarious.

                    LONGWORTH
She indicated to me that it was.

                    JUSTIN
Maybe she just indicated that to
you to mess with you. And what's
that got to do with the woman
without the head?

                    LONGWORTH
What's with everyone and that
question? It's how a police
investigation works. That's what
we do, we ask questions. Sometimes
direct, sometimes indirect, it
doesn't matter if they make sense
to you, half the time they don't
make sense to me.

                    JUSTIN
I know she's lying because I know
for a fact a guy she did before
me.

                    LONGWORTH
How do you know he's not lying?

                    JUSTIN
Because he was my brother.

                    LONGWORTH
What do you mean, was? Is your
brother dead?

                    JUSTIN
Yeah, he's dead. Got clipped on
his motorcycle by a tourist on
State Road 301. At Interlake and
301, where the light is now. Put
that friggin' light up right after
it happened, like some friggin'
reminder to me, so that every time
I drive by I get to remember how
he got mangled by some minivan
driving asswipe from friggin'
Maine.

>   LONGWORTH
>   Well at least you've worked
>   through it.

Justin glares at Longworth.

>   LONGWORTH
>   I'm gonna need to ask you a few
>   more questions, so don't leave
>   town without checking with me
>   first.

>   JUSTIN
>   Why?

>   LONGWORTH
>   I'm pretty sure we just covered
>   that.

Longworth gets up and leaves. Off Justin...

EXT. HIGHWAY INTERSECTION - S.R. 301 -
NIGHT

CLOSE on a TRAFFIC LIGHT, burning green in
a moonless night.

ECU of the instrument, the screen filled
with green. Emitting an electronic BUZZ.
The light shifts from green to yellow,
angle widening now to include it. Then on
again to red.

The light glows, instrument swinging in a
light ocean breeze.

WIDER

A vehicle, a sedan, comes to a full stop
at the intersection.

INT. LONGWORTH'S CAR - NIGHT

Longworth at the wheel, annoyed he caught the light. He looks left and right, even more annoyed to realize there's no traffic in either direction.

He waits, checking his bandaged hand, squeezing and unsqueezing his grip, wincing slightly from discomfort.

He looks at the light, still red. When something at the curb of the intersection catches his eye.

A "shrine" at the base of the traffic light. Beer cans and liquor bottles, candles, notes, flowers, relatively fresh.

Longworth gets out of the car and steps to the shrine.

He kneels to read a few notes and cards, all a loving tribute to "Lane," live fast and die hard, etc.

Longworth looks up at the street signs at the intersection.

State Road 301 and Interlake Boulevard.

A car HORN blasts -- some idiot behind his idling car, pissed to be waiting behind a light that's turned green.

                                        FADE OUT:

                    END OF ACT TWO

ACT THREE

FADE IN:

EXT. RANDALL'S - BAR - NIGHT

Shoe-horned into the middle of downtown
Tampa Bay.

INT. RANDALL'S - BAR - NIGHT

The place busy with a nighttime crowd. The
MUSIC jazz-infused, the vibe, half drunk
and sexy. Longworth enters, carrying a
file. He looks around the bar, sees someone
through the crowd, in the distance by the
pinball machines.

He starts over, then stops when he sees
Ogletree sitting alone at the bar, staring
into a highball.

                    LONGWORTH
          Hey.

                    OGLETREE
          Oh. Hey.

                    LONGWORTH
          What are you drinking?

                    OGLETREE
          Bourbon.

                    LONGWORTH
          You don't drink bourbon.

                    OGLETREE
          Sometimes I do. Have a seat.

LONGWORTH

I'm looking for Carlos. His wife
said he likes to come here for the
old school pinballs.

OGLETREE

Haven't seen him.

LONGWORTH

He's right there.

Ogletree looks to where Longworth is
pointing.

OGLETREE

I didn't even see him.

LONGWORTH

What was the name of that kid's
brother?

OGLETREE

What kid?

LONGWORTH

Justin. Was it Lane?

OGLETREE

Lane? Maybe. Yeah. Why?

LONGWORTH

There's a shrine for him at the
light at State Road 301 and
Interlake. When was that accident
that killed him?

OGLETREE

I don't know. A year ago, maybe.

                    LONGWORTH
          To the day?

                    OGLETREE
          Maybe. About that.

                    LONGWORTH
          Are you okay?

                    OGLETREE
          Yeah. Just fighting with my wife,
          is all.

                    LONGWORTH
          You guys don't fight.

                    OGLETREE
          We don't very often. She went to
          her sister's - whatever. Big drama
          queen, right? You want a drink?

                    LONGWORTH
          Let me take care of this first.

                    OGLETREE
          Sure, sure. I'll be here.

ANGLE ON CARLOS

Slamming into a pinball machine as
Longworth approaches.

                    LONGWORTH
          Why didn't you tell me there was a
          tooth?

                    CARLOS
          What are you talking about?

Longworth pulls out the Medical Exam
protocol.

LONGWORTH
It says you pulled a tooth from
the vic.

CARLOS
A cuspid. From the alligator.

LONGWORTH
Why didn't you tell me?

CARLOS
What difference does it make?

LONGWORTH
Carlos, a tooth can tell us all
kinds of things.

CARLOS
About the alligator.

LONGWORTH
Size, sex, migration...

CARLOS
Of the alligator.

LONGWORTH
Digestive system, is it fast,
slow, one week, two weeks?

CARLOS
Okay.

LONGWORTH
It's been three days, maybe the
head is still intact.

CARLOS
Are you out of your mind? How are
you gonna find the one alligator in

36

a swamp of alligators who fed on
our Jane Doe?

> LONGWORTH

With the tooth.

> CARLOS

No wonder your partner hates you.

> LONGWORTH

Don't be so lazy, Carlos.

> CARLOS

Did you just call me lazy?

> LONGWORTH

When's the tox screen scheduled?

> CARLOS

Tomorrow.

> LONGWORTH

I want to go with you.

> CARLOS

I'm not taking you to the lab with
me.

> LONGWORTH

Why not?

> CARLOS

The last time I did that they had
a problem with you.

> LONGWORTH

So. Professional courtesy.

                    CARLOS
          Professional courtesy? You told
          them they had their head up their
          ass.

                    LONGWORTH
          They do. Or they did. I have no
          idea if it's a recurring problem
          or not. I'll keep an open mind.

Longworth heads off before Carlos can
object. Carlos slugs more coins in,
cajoling the pinball machine back to life.

Longworth returns to where Ogletree was
sitting, his empty bourbon and a beer sit
there. Money on the bar to pay for both.

                    LONGWORTH
          Excuse me? What happened to the
          guy who was sitting here?

                    BARTENDER
          Said he was tired. Beer's for you.

INT. UNIVERSITY OF SOUTH FLORIDA - DAY

Longworth with DANIEL GREEN, 23, grad
student in Herpetology, who looks at the
alligator tooth in a plastic baggie --

                    GREEN
          Melanosuchus, would be my guess.
          Genus, phylum, can't be certain
          without more research. But all
          members of the chordata family are
          territorial.

                    LONGWORTH
          And digestion is what, long, short?

                        GREEN
        Very slow, like ten days. Let me
        hang on to this, do some blood
        work, I can probably give you
        size, sex, coloring. Will that
        help?

Longworth hands the kid his business card.

                        LONGWORTH
        Call me.

EXT. CALLIE'S HOUSE - BACK PORCH LANAI -
NIGHT

Longworth and Callie. The case file on a
table between them as she studies a crime
photo of the DRESS the vic wore --

                        CALLIE
        J.T. Landers? Never heard of it.

                        LONGWORTH
        It's a regional clothing chain
        operating out of the Southwest.
        I'm not much on the fashion habits
        of women, but does that look like
        something you'd order online?

                        CALLIE
        Depends. Was I exceedingly drunk?

He grins as she sets the photo down.

                        LONGWORTH
        The victim also had high levels
        of capsicum in her stomach from
        eating spicy foods.

                    CALLIE
Like Southwest spicy?

                    LONGWORTH
And trace amounts of tricresyl
phosphate in her lungs, a
neurotoxin found in motor oil that
humans get by breathing recycled
air, like on most commercial
airline flights.

                    CALLIE
So you're thinking she's a
tourist.

                    LONGWORTH
Tourist, in town on business.
Although I'm trying to avoid
thinking anything specific just
yet.

                    CALLIE
That would explain why she hasn't
been reported missing. Traveling
alone, family back in Phoenix...
        (off his look)
-- not to suggest anything
specific. Is she a mom? If she is,
I'm sure one of her kids is trying
to get a hold of her.

                    LONGWORTH
See, I said the same thing to my
guy, and he said I was nuts.

                    CALLIE
Oh, you have a guy?

> LONGWORTH
>
> He's not my own personal guy. I
> have to share him with the rest of
> the county.

Callie is mildly amused despite her best
efforts.

> CALLIE
>
> So you were shot by your captain
> for not sleeping with his wife and
> ended up in Palm Glade.

> LONGWORTH
>
> More or less. Got a little money
> for it. Not a fortune as it turns
> out, but thanks to a rash of short
> sells, enough to land comfortably.
> But trust me, if it ever gets too
> busy or too dangerous, I'm out of
> here.
>   (off her grin)
> Do you have a beer or something?

> CALLIE
>
> Because I find you mildly amusing?

> LONGWORTH
>
> Or, because I'm thirsty.

> CALLIE
>
> Look. I don't want my son to think
> there's something going on here.

> LONGWORTH
>
> Can't we just tell him there's
> nothing going on as I sip my beer?

                    CALLIE
         Technically, I'm still married...

Longworth, stealing a quick look to the
ring on her finger.

                    CALLIE
         Yeah sorry, I wash my hands about
         a million times a shift, so...
                 (hence no ring earlier)
         -- and Jeff likes to dialogue with
         his father about my activities.

                    LONGWORTH
         Where is he?

                    CALLIE
         Well he's supposed to be in his
         room not doing his homework. But
         my guess is he's spying on us.

                    LONGWORTH
         I meant his father. The man you're
         technically still married to?

Callie takes a beat.

                    CALLIE
            Raiford.

That   a really bad prison in Florida.

                    LONGWORTH
         Impressive.

                    CALLIE
         Yup.
              (beat)
         Jeff?
              (then over her shoulder)

Jeff?!

Then, from inside the house --

                    JEFF (O.S.)
          What?

                    CALLIE
          Homework.

                    JEFF
          I finished.

                    CALLIE
          All of it?

                    JEFF
          What part of finished is confusing
          to you?

She looks at Longworth. That's my son. As
Jeff joins them.

                    JEFF
          What are you guys talking about?

                    CALLIE
          Like you haven't been listening.

                    JEFF
          Is that the woman you guys found?
               (snatching up one of the photos)
          Cool. What happened to her head?

                    CALLIE
          Okay, these are going bye-bye.

She snatches up the photos, stuffs them in
the file.

                    JEFF
          Did she offer you a beer?

                    LONGWORTH
          No. And I even asked nicely.

                      JEFF
          I'll get it.

                    CALLIE
          He won't be here long enough. Now
          say good night and go finish your
          homework.

A look from Mom cinching it. Jeff shrugging
his apology.

                      JEFF
          Sorry about the beer.

Longworth gives him a smile, and Jeff
returns inside. After a beat, when she's
sure he's gone --

                    CALLIE
          Armed Robbery. My husband.

                    LONGWORTH
          I wasn't going to ask.

                    CALLIE
          Now is there anything else, or can
          we say good night?

                    LONGWORTH
          When did you lose your virginity?

                    CALLIE
          Okay, look at the time.

                    LONGWORTH
          No, I'm serious. One of my
          suspects may or may not have used
          hers to wrap some guy around her

finger. Now, I've heard rumors about you people...
          (off her look)
-- is it possible to "lose your virginity" to more than one guy in order to manipulate him?

                    CALLIE
Sure. I lost mine three or four times.

                    LONGWORTH
Really? And we just fall for that?

                    CALLIE
Every time. And are you sure he wasn't using *her*?

                    LONGWORTH
Not entirely. But you haven't seen this girl. And he was pretty hammered.

                    CALLIE
So you've never been so drunk you couldn't quite piece together an evening you'd rather forget?

                    LONGWORTH
Never.
          (off her look, beat)
And he did lose his brother to a motorcycle accident with a tourist.

                    CALLIE
Ugh, I remember that. That shrine. Totally freaks Jeff out.
          (beat)

Revenge is a pretty strong motive.

                    LONGWORTH
But whose? I mean, was he setting
the girl up as his alibi? Or was
she using her sexuality against
him. Lying about her virginity.

                    CALLIE
How old is she?

                    LONGWORTH
Sixteen.

                    CALLIE
Oh yeah, I'd go with lying. And if
the question is, do we lie to guys
to get you to think we're giving
you something special so we can
manipulate the hell out of you?
Yeah. We do that, too.

Off Longworth, letting that sink in.

EXT. PALM GLADE PRESERVE - FISHEATING
CREEK - DAY

The surface teeming with bouncing, buzzing,
annoying insects.

                    GREEN (O.S.)
Caiman, female, about four years
old. Between nine and ten feet.

Longworth and Daniel Green on the bank.
Green scanning the creek with a pair of
binoculars.

                    LONGWORTH
Not bad from just one tooth.

                    GREEN
          Go you one better, caiman aren't
          indigenous. Probably someone's pet
          who let it loose when she got too
          big. Won't be the only gator in
          the area but she'll definitely be
          the only caiman. Wait. Here we
          go...

The point of view shifts to binocular...

A pair of eyes drifting ahead of a spine,
specific markings which he enthusiastically
describes --

                    GREEN (O.C.)
          Broad snout, bony ridge over the
          eyes, definitely caiman. Female
          coloring, easy ten footer...

When BAM! The lens jolts, taking us back
out to --

Green recoiling from the report from
Longworth's gun.

                    LONGWORTH
          That's the one, right?

Green stares at Longworth in disbelief.
Stunned.

                    GREEN
          That animal is protected.

                    LONGWORTH
          Then how come I had such a clear
          shot?

Longworth holsters his gun. Off Green,
yawning his hearing back...   FADE OUT.

                 END OF ACT THREE

<u>ACT FOUR</u>

FADE IN:

INT. LAB - DAY

A ten-foot CAIMAN lies on top of a surgical table. Daniel Green over it, marking an area near the stomach with a red marker.

Carlos and Longworth, off to the side, Carlos pissed there's an alligator on his table.

                    CARLOS
          Unorthodox? Try nuts. I'm not
          autopsing an alligator, get that
          thing off my table.

                    LONGWORTH
          Caiman. Then let the kid do it.

                    CARLOS
          Right, and Chain of Evidence goes
          out the window.

                    LONGWORTH
          See, you think I'm right.

                    CARLOS
          I think you're nuts but we've been
          over that already.

ANGLE ON AUTOPSY TABLE

Daniel Green is over the caiman, gestures along a section of the reptile's belly marked with red, as they step up.

                    GREEN
          Tubal absorption runs along the

>   length of the thorax. Anything
>   this guy's eaten in the last ten
>   days will be right along here.

>   LONGWORTH
>   Look at that? All marked up for
>   you and everything.

>   GREEN
>   Thanks for letting me observe, Dr.
>   Sanchez. I really appreciate it.

>   CARLOS
>   Yeah. No problem.

Carlos shoots Longworth a look, takes a
scalpel, inserts it along the marking. A
tough hide requiring a great deal of effort
as he saws along the cut line.

>   GREEN
>   The caiman latirostris is pretty
>   efficient as a predator. Eats fish,
>   turtles...small land creatures
>   like raccoon, possum...pretty much
>   anything that ventures into its
>   waters, especially if it's nesting
>   or just gave birth...

The cut finished, Carlos inserts a gloved
hand into the opening.

>   GREEN
>   Their enzyme production is really
>   low cause they have like no immune
>   system - basically they never get
>   sick, so it gets pretty backed up
>   in there...

He begins removing fleshy debris, which

Green identifies as Carlos pulls out,
dropping it into a blue container --

> GREEN
>> -- catfish...I'd say brim or perch
>> maybe...box turtle...

Which Carlos drops it in, feels briefly
around inside, then --

> CARLOS
>> Okay. That's it.

> GREEN
>> No, there's more.
>>> (off Carlos' look)
>> I can feel it.
>>> (he feels, confirming)
>> Yeah, definitely.

Beat. Carlos looks at Longworth, runs his
hand back inside.

When he feels something and stops. Adjusts
his slippery grip and pulls it out. Covered
in blood and partially digested.

But clearly a human jawbone.

> GREEN
>> Oh man. Sweet...a jawbone.

Carlos, half amazed, half annoyed.

INT. FLORIDA HIGHWAY PATROL - OFFICE - DAY

Ogletree at his desk, annoyed and groaning
over his keyboard.

                    LONGWORTH
Anything popping with that?

                    OGLETREE
It keeps asking me if I want to
download a new version.

                    LONGWORTH
Ignore it. Most departments work
off Adobe three-point-nine years
ago anyway.

                    OGLETREE
Tourists, transients, illegals -
this is Florida. Thousands of
visitors from all over the world
pass through this time of year...

                    LONGWORTH
Just focus on the ones who've been
reported missing.

                    OGLETREE
What if they haven't?

                    LONGWORTH
Family, co-workers, friends,
eventually someone calls it in.

                    OGLETREE
And then there's HIPPA rules...

                    LONGWORTH
We have some leg work to do
before we start asking for dental
records. Pace yourself. It'll come
together.

>   OGLETREE
>   You could help.

>   LONGWORTH
>   I found the jawbone.

Not what he wanted to hear. Longworth
throws him a bone.

>   LONGWORTH
>   I saved you a trip to the high
>   school...

Longworth fans open a high school yearbook
showing him a page of graduating seniors.
One in particular --

>   LONGWORTH
>   Lane Brussard, class of '02, and
>   I quote: "Okeechobee Southerners
>   Are Sub-Human". A quote that's
>   been popping up all over the high
>   school this past week.

Ogletree refusing to give it up.

>   OGLETREE
>   We still don't know what it means.

>   LONGWORTH
>   It means the one-year anniversary
>   of his brother being killed by a
>   tourist had not gone forgotten.

INT. ROBBIE'S RAW BAR - DAY

Justin daytime drinking and having lunch.
Looks up as Longworth sits down across
from him, without an invitation.

                    LONGWORTH
          So I figured out who's been
          painting on the sides of buildings
          around here.

Justin looks at him for a beat, then goes
back to eating.

                    LONGWORTH
          Your brother.

                    JUSTIN
          That's not funny.

                    LONGWORTH
          I don't mean your brother per se.
          I mean someone who loved your
          brother. Who thought he was a hero
          worth remembering. Someone who
          looked up to him. That's who did
          it.

                    JUSTIN
          He had a lot of people like that.

                    LONGWORTH
          Yeah, I'm not hearing that. I'm
          hearing he was kind of a moody
          little dipshit. It's all about
          him. That guy.

                    JUSTIN
          He could be that.

                    LONGWORTH
          Which can put some people off.

Justin glances up at that, but right back
down to eat.

LONGWORTH

So here's what I think is going
on. And you tell me where I've got
it wrong.
          (beat)
You hate tourists. I mean, who
doesn't, right? But unlike the
rest of us, you have a really good
reason. And knowing that, I'd be
kind of an idiot not to pursue the
possibility that you lured one of
those annoying asswipes into a
situation, killed her, dumped her
body in the swamp, then dragged
poor Erin into it after the fact
so she could witness you "finding"
her headless body, how's that?

Justin, head down, pushing his food around,
listening.

LONGWORTH

Only that's not what happened.
I mean, you might have done it,
I've been wrong before. But I
just don't see it. See the thing
about murder? Is you really have
to be able to keep it together
to get away with it, and I don't
know, something about the way a
kid like you is able to sit here
sawing away at Robbie's chicken
fried steak just doesn't say to me
that three nights ago you killed a
woman and fed her to an alligator.
And for my deal, if I have loose
ends or something doesn't fit or

add up? Then I really haven't
eliminated anything. And murder is
all about elimination. So while I
could be wrong, I just don't see
it. Now what I do see you doing is
spray painting Okeechobee whatever
the hell on the side of a few
buildings so no one will forget
your brother. Will you give me
that?

Justin looks up. Stares a beat.

> JUSTIN
> Okay.

> LONGWORTH
> Good. And was it your idea or your
> girlfriend's to plaster it all
> over the high school?

> JUSTIN
> She's not my girlfriend.

> LONGWORTH
> Not your girlfriend.

> JUSTIN
> We're just hanging out.

> LONGWORTH
> Hanging out with a sixteen-year-
> old.

> JUSTIN
> I mean. We just. We were both...
> thinking about him. I was drunk.
> I don't know. We just wanted to
> remember him...

Justin stops, not sure where he stands
here.

> JUSTIN
> She told me she checked. I thought
> she was telling me the truth.

Longworth lets that worry sit on his head
for a beat.

> LONGWORTH
> She was, son. It's sixteen.
> (beat)
> Sorry, kid.

Longworth gets up and leaves. Off Justin --

INT. OGLETREE'S HOUSE - KITCHEN - DAY (OR
EXTERIOR SPIGOT)

Ogletree tending to something at the sink,
on his cell phone.

> OGLETREE
> Well yeah, he was drunk. That's
> not exactly news.

INT. LONGWORTH'S CAR - TRAVELING - DAY

Longworth driving, on his cell phone.
INTERCUT as necessary.

> LONGWORTH
> Slept on a blanket by the creek
> most of the night. Barely
> remembers trying before passing
> out completely. And sure as
> hell can't account for Erin's
> whereabouts.

                    OGLETREE
          Bet he remembers tagging half the
          damn county.
                    (beat)
          I've got calls in to all the major
          airlines, checking passenger lists
          on flights from Flagstaff, Phoenix,
          Albuquerque...

                    LONGWORTH
          I could've done that...

                    OGLETREE
          I said I'd handle it.

Said a little emphatically, which Longworth
notes...

                    LONGWORTH
          And the entire school was tagged.
          So we should probably check to see
          if any of their female teachers or
          employees have failed to show up
          for work. Eliminate by profile...

                    OGLETREE
          Oh, we do profiles now.

                    LONGWORTH
          Approximate height, weight, age.
          No children.

Ogletree annoyed at being told how to do
his job.

                    OGLETREE
          Not my first picnic, you know.
          Still say she'll turn out to be a
          tourist.

                    LONGWORTH
          Bad cop work sticking to one
          theory, mi amigo.

When ARF ARF ARF and we WIDEN to see
Ogletree lowering the fresh bowl of water
he just filled to a yappy piece of shit
white Maltese.

                    LONGWORTH
          Did you bring your dog to work?

                    OGLETREE
          Nah, swung by the house. Promised
          the wife I'd look after it. Last
          thing I need is to come home to
          the neighbors pounding on the door
          that the damn thing barked all
          day.
               (beat)
          I'll check with the school and get
          back to you.

And Ogletree hangs up. Off Longworth...

EXT. FISHEATING CREEK - SERIES OF DISSOLVES
- DAY

Longworth with his 9-iron, sifting through
the detritus of a local hangout - beer and
soda cans, crumpled packs of cigarettes,
cigarette butts, condoms, lotto scratchers,
a Slushie cup and straw.

When he sees something near the bank of the
creek. Steps for it, stopping and kneeling
closer to get a better look.

An area of WET MUCK, FLAT and TACKY from
the SOLES of FLAT, HEAVY SHOES. He looks at
the bottom of his Vans, checking its TREAD

and PRINTS in the muck against the prints left by the flat-soled shoes.

He looks back around, listening, turning things over. Sees and then moves for something back by the weeds. Picks it up.

A SALES RECEIPT, from a local package store named Darby's. Which he looks at. Over which --

> LONGWORTH (V.O.)
> A blow pop, two Red Bulls, a bag of corn nuts and lotto tickets.

INT. DARBY'S PACKAGE STORE - DAY

Longworth talking to the genius CLERK behind the counter.

> LONGWORTH
> She buy anything else?

The CLERK stuck on his photo of hot Erin, doesn't respond.

> LONGWORTH
> Beer, whisky, maybe offer to have sex with you?

That gets his attention.

> CLERK
> What?

> LONGWORTH
> Did she buy anything else? Maybe came in with someone?

> CLERK
> No. She came alone. Our ATM was down, she asked where the nearest

one was. I told her across town.

                    LONGWORTH
          Notice anything odd or suspicious
          about her behavior?

                    CLERK
          Seemed kind of pissed off about
          something. A little wired for two
          o'clock in the morning...

The clerk stuck on the photo.

                    LONGWORTH
          You can keep that if you want?

                    CLERK
          Really?

Longworth looks at him like "no you can't
keep it," snatches it back, then leaves
with his purchases.

EXT. CONVENIENCE STORE - MINUTES LATER

Longworth comes out, gets in his sedan.
Stops. Sees Jeff and some rough looking,
older kids, smoking, jacking around on the
side of the building.

Jeff sees Longworth. They look at each
other. Jeff takes a long drag from a
cigarette, blows smoke. Goes back to his
buddies.

INT. TAMPA GRACE MEDICAL CENTER - DAY

Longworth with Callie, at her desk. Callie
applies iodine tincture to his wound,
distracted by work, studies...

                    CALLIE
          The girl bought lotto tickets?

                    LONGWORTH
          A blow pop, two Red Bulls, a bag
          of corn nuts and lotto tickets.

She re-dresses his wound as he contemplates
their meaning.

                    LONGWORTH
          He was drunk and passed out - she
          had to do something...
                    (beat)
          Jeff doesn't drink those does he?

                    CALLIE
          Lives on 'em.

                    LONGWORTH
          You know what's in that stuff?

                    CALLIE
          No. Do you?

Said busy and impatient.

                    LONGWORTH
          They make you pee like a race
          horse. Two of 'em, she'd be up all
          night.

                    CALLIE
          I haven't noticed Jeff doing an
          inordinate amount of peeing.

                    LONGWORTH
          Am I bothering you?

                    CALLIE
          Yes. I'm busy. Don't take it
          personally. I have a test on
          Monday.

Finished with his bandage, she returns to
her textbook. Longworth testing his grip,
taking practice swings.

                    LONGWORTH
          I don't know. A sixteen-year-old
          killer? Statistical long shot.
          But she did lie about leaving.
          Maybe lied to Justin - still don't
          understand why you guys do that.

                    CALLIE
          Because we can. It's special. Or
          you think so.

                    LONGWORTH
          You don't think it's special?

                    CALLIE
          I did at the time.

She goes back to her studies. Back to his
practice swings.

                    LONGWORTH
          I saw Jeff. Hanging with some older
          boys.

                    CALLIE
          I know his friends, they're okay.
          Bored maybe. Was he smoking?

                    LONGWORTH
          No.

                    CALLIE
          You wouldn't tell me if he was.
          You can't talk Jeff into doing
          something he doesn't want to do.
          If he's into something wrong, he
          got there by himself. That's the
          best you can hope for.

                    LONGWORTH
          You've got to read this whole
          book?

                    CALLIE
          Eventually.

                    LONGWORTH
          Maybe I'll take him to a movie.

     She looks up from her reading.

                    LONGWORTH
          You barely have time for yourself.
          I'm sure he's bored.

                    CALLIE
          Look. Don't police my son. Neither
          one of us are huge fans of your
          line of work.

                    LONGWORTH
          I guess I understand that.

     She looks at him, goes back to her book,
     when his cell phone rings. He moves off to
     answer it.

                    LONGWORTH
          Hey. What do you got?

EXT. FDLE SUB-STATION - DAY

Graffiti on the wall, Ogletree on his cell --

                    OGLETREE
          The high school hasn't reported
          any of their regular female
          teachers missing. However...

INT. HOSPITAL - CLOSE ON LONGWORTH - DAY

Longworth on his cell. INTERCUT as
Longworth cuts him off --

                    LONGWORTH
          She doesn't have to be a regular
          employee, she could be --

                    OGLETREE
          Damn it, Jim, for once would you
          just let me finish my thought.

                    LONGWORTH
          Sorry.

                    OGLETREE
          But there was a substitute teacher
          scheduled to teach last week who
          never showed up, and hasn't been
          heard from since.

                    LONGWORTH
          Does this substitute teacher have
          a name?

                    OGLETREE
          Yeah, Salazar. Gina Salazar.
                  (waiting for his attaboy)
          Jim? Jim?

Ogletree realizing Longworth has hung up.

A low GROWL takes us down to find the
Maltese, at the end of a leash --

> OGLETREE
> Hate you too, you little shit.

Summing up their relationship as he hurries
the dog along to do its business.

EXT. INTERSECTION - S.R. 301 AND INTERLAKE
BLVD. - NIGHT

We are CLOSE on the LOCKET, opened now to
reveal the person inside. LANE Broussard,
Justin's older brother. Held gently in
the palm of a soft hand. Then lowered to
reveal --

The Shrine to Lane, his photo ringed
by flowers, candles, and booze bottles;
messages from those who love and miss him.
But none more than --

ERIN, who sits alone, cross-legged at the
base of the shrine. When her shadow is
joined by another.

> LONGWORTH (O.C.)
> Sucks.

She turns to see Longworth there.

> LONGWORTH
> Letting someone go.

EXT. CONVENIENCE STORE - NIGHT

Erin alone in Longworth's unmarked sedan.
She watches as he exits the store, walks
over, hands her a pack of cigarettes he
just bought through the window.

                    ERIN
        Thanks.

                    LONGWORTH
        Just not in the car.

She nods, pops in the lighter. Continues
their conversation.

                    ERIN
        The night he was killed, he was
        coming to see me. Lane. He just
        got off work at Pizza Hut and I
        told him to meet me here. Had to
        sneak out cause I was only fifteen.

The lighter pops and she lights her
cigarette, blowing smoke as she gets out
of the car.

                    ERIN
        I told him to wear his Calvin
        Klein cause I didn't want him
        smellin' like Pizza Hut my first
        time. I was real nervous. Maybe he
        was too, I don't know. Or maybe
        his mind was just elsewhere.

Longworth watches the young woman smoke.
Doubts his mind was elsewhere.

                    ERIN
        I've never told Justin this. But
        he and Lane look really alike. Not
        in the face, but like their hands
        and the way they sit on a car and
        their voice. It's weird on the
        phone. I thought with Calvin Klein
        and whatever, it might seem like
        it was him. Like if Lane hadn't

been hit on his motorcycle that
night and we finally got to do it.
I really wanted it to be him.

                    LONGWORTH
          He was a surrogate.

She looks at him. Doesn't know what that
means.

                    LONGWORTH
          You used Justin in place of his
          brother.

Erin shrugs yeah I guess...

                    LONGWORTH
          He didn't like that. Subbing for
          his brother.

                    ERIN
          Threw a whole brand new bottle of
          CK in the creek.

                    LONGWORTH
          That why you left?

                    ERIN
          Partly. He was too drunk by then
          anyway. Tried for like fifteen
          minutes. You'd think he'd stop
          drinking but I think trying made
          him drink more. When he passed out
          I just left. Tried to stay gone
          a long time. Went and got my dad
          his lotto scratchers. I was mad,
          I guess. Wanted Justin to worry
          about me.

She smokes.

                    LONGWORTH
          How long were you gone?

                      ERIN
          I don't know. Hour maybe.

                    LONGWORTH
          So you left twice?

                      ERIN
     No.

                    LONGWORTH
          Then you were gone a lot longer
          than an hour.

She looks at him. Smokes.

                    LONGWORTH
          You came here just after two in
          the morning. Then used the ATM at
          the Bank in the strip mall at the
          other end of town.

                      ERIN
          I forgot to get my dad his
          scratchers and didn't have enough
          money cause I spent what he gave
          me on beer for Justin.

                    LONGWORTH
          Not that withdrawal, the one you
          made for the maximum three hundred
          dollars at four-thirty in the
          morning.

Beat.

                    ERIN
        I went twice. I told you I was
        trying to make him worry about me.

                    LONGWORTH
        If you were so mad at him why
        didn't you just go home?

She smokes, shrugs.

                    LONGWORTH
        So you still have the money?

                    ERIN
        No. It's gone. I spent it.

                    LONGWORTH
        You remember Gina Salazar? She
        sometimes substitute teaches at
        your school.

                    ERIN
        No.

                    LONGWORTH
        Yeah, she served you with
        detention for writing Okeechobee
        Southerners are Sub-Human over her
        assignment.

She smokes, shrugs.

                    ERIN
        Okay.

                    LONGWORTH
        She's missing.

                              FADE OUT.

            END OF ACT FOUR

ACT FIVE

FADE IN:

EXT. FISHEATING CREEK - DAY

Longworth tracking along the edge of the
creek. Stomping tall weeds, his eyes
searching the uneven earth distressed by
clumps of grass and cragged by cypress
knee. Then stops.

Kneeling to the wet earth, and another area
of MUCK made FLAT and TACKY by the SOLES
of HEAVY, flat soled SHOES.

He rises, moves on ahead as we DISSOLVE
through...

EXT. FISHEATING CREEK - ELSEWHERE - DAY

Longworth tramps through the weeds, seeing
something in the creek. He bends to lift
it out of the water.

A brand new, unopened bottle of Calvin
Klein for Men. He studies the bottle, and
its meaning. Sniffs it. Deciding --

                    LONGWORTH
          I guess that's better than Pizza
          Hut.

When interest in his find is broken by a
whoop of excitement coming from the bank
across the creek.

                    JEFF
          Hey. I got one.

Jeff on the shore, reeling in his catch.

                    LONGWORTH
          I'm impressed.
                 (watching the kid's joy)
          What kind of fish is that?

                      JEFF
          Shiner.

                    LONGWORTH
          I thought you said fishing was for
          losers?

Jeff grins at the fish, unhooks it --

                      JEFF
          Aren't I contaminating a crime
          scene?

                    LONGWORTH
          You're helping me interview
          witnesses.

                      JEFF
          He doesn't look like he saw
          anything.

                    LONGWORTH
          Thank him for his time and send
          him on his way.

Which he does, when Longworth's cell phone
rings. He checks the caller I.D., answers
it --

                    LONGWORTH
          What'd you find out?
                 (listens a beat)
          Yeah, okay. Thanks. Sorry about
          working you on a Sunday.

He hangs up. A little quiet. Over which --

> OGLETREE (V.O.)
> So the teacher's not missing?

EXT. OGLETREE HOUSE - BACKYARD - BARBEQUE - DAY

Ogletree at the grill, Longworth nearby, a beer in hand.

> LONGWORTH
> Ran off with some guy. Husband was pissed I even called. Told me to shove his wife's dental records up my ass.

> OGLETREE
> The girl still lied.

> LONGWORTH
> Yeah. Sometimes they do that.

Beat. Longworth hoists his beer to their Sunday ritual.

> LONGWORTH
> Thanks for keeping our streak alive.

> OGLETREE
> It's just burgers.

> LONGWORTH
> Under the circumstances I would've understood. I know I've been treating you like my secretary.

> OGLETREE
> We got the jawbone. I'll stay on it.

Ogletree clearly feeling underappreciated.

                    LONGWORTH
          You know, you might feel better if
          you get out whatever it is that's
          bothering you.

Ogletree takes a beat. Not very good at
the feelings thing.

                    OGLETREE
          The thing is. Well. I never
          intended to play this card. I
          mean, yeah, we're partners, but
          technically, with seniority, I am
          your supervisor. Your boss.

                    LONGWORTH
          I guess I know that.

                    OGLETREE
          I've given you an awful lot of
          latitude. Too much, maybe. How
          else was I supposed to evaluate
          your worthiness? But hell, you
          won't even wear the uniform.

                    LONGWORTH
          I wear the badge.
               (off his look)
          You know, in spirit.

                    OGLETREE
          I've been doing a good job here
          for a long time.

                    LONGWORTH
          I'm just trying to work in.

> OGLETREE
> I'm having trouble with that. You
> being here. I can't say it's fair
> for either one of us. Why should I
> feel like I'm not up to the job?

Ogletree presses the burgers, trying to
get this out.

> LONGWORTH
> What are you doing?

> OGLETREE
> I'm trying to tell you that it's
> not working out.

> LONGWORTH
> I mean to the meat. You're
> smashing the burgers, that dries
> 'em out.

Ogletree takes a beat.

> LONGWORTH
> Look, I appreciate you telling
> me how you feel. I know you and
> Janice are fighting and I know
> that's not easy for you. But you
> can't really expect me to be
> sloppy just so you can feel good
> about yourself.

A beat. Ogletree smashes the burgers.
Juices escape amid sizzle and flame.

> OGLETREE
> Burgers are done.

But neither man moves.

> LONGWORTH
> When's Janice coming home?

> OGLETREE
> She didn't say.

> LONGWORTH
> She didn't say.
> (beat)
> She must be really mad at you.

A long beat, during which Ogletree does not respond.

> OGLETREE
> I need to chop an onion.

Ogletree heads for the house. Longworth watches as his partner disappears inside.

INT. OGLETREE HOUSE - KITCHEN - DAY

Ogletree grabs an onion and a chopping board. Opens a drawer, fishes around for a knife, then stops.

He moves to another drawer. Opens it slowly and looks inside.

EXT. OGLETREE HOUSE - BACKYARD - DAY

Longworth has the meat off the grill, fanning off flies.

> LONGWORTH
> Better get to these quick.

> OGLETREE
> Do you even carry your service revolver?

Longworth stops. Turns to see Ogletree

with his gun on him.

> OGLETREE
> Wasn't one in your vehicle, I
> looked.

There is a beat. Longworth getting that
he's pretty screwed.

> LONGWORTH
> It's Sunday, Mike. What do I need
> a gun for?

> OGLETREE
> You got my wife's dental records?
> Without telling me. What kind of
> cop looks into his partner without
> telling him?

> LONGWORTH
> Your wife was missing.

Ogletree looks at him. Guess he sees his
point.

> LONGWORTH
> Well that, and your shoes.

> OGLETREE
> My shoes?

Which we look down to see. Clunky, flat
soled FLORIDA HIGHWAY PATROL issued shoes.

> LONGWORTH
> Which were all over the crime
> scene -- to say nothing of the
> M.E.'s report, which confirmed not
> only the victim's natural Florida
> tan, but also that she'd never had

children...
            (off the dog barking)
-- no doubt settling for a dog...
which you hate, but cared for
anyway so the neighbors wouldn't
get suspicious...

                    OGLETREE
Jim.

                    LONGWORTH
-- then of course there's the
capsicum we found in her stomach -
evidence that she'd recently eaten
spicy Southwestern food - and
the fact that just hours before
she was killed, she'd been on a
commercial flight - wearing a dress
she bought while visiting her
sister...

                    OGLETREE
Jim.

                    LONGWORTH
-- I mean, to be perfectly honest,
amigo, when you stop and think
about it, you were so incredibly
bad at this...

                    OGLETREE
I said okay!

                    LONGWORTH
I feel kind of stupid it took me
so long.

A long beat. Neither man moves, as
Longworth brings it home.

                    LONGWORTH
          Your wife didn't go to her
          sister's because you had a
          fight, Mike. She flew back from
          Albuquerque to tell you that she
          was leaving you...
                    (a sad beat, then)
          And you had a fight.

A fight that led to murder, which Ogletree
is not denying.

                    LONGWORTH
          So what are we going to do?

                    OGLETREE
          I killed my wife. Mutilated the
          woman I slept next to for sixteen
          years, you think I won't shoot
          you?

                    LONGWORTH
          I'm kind of hoping you won't.

                    OGLETREE
          I mean, look at you. You dress
          like a clown. Treat the job like
          an inconvenience.

                    LONGWORTH
          It is kind of a pain in the ass.

                    OGLETREE
          Why should I take shit from you?

                    LONGWORTH
          Cause I'm a better cop than you.

There is a beat. Ogletree trying to find
his footing.

                    OGLETREE
        I tried, Jim. I really did. Things
        didn't always suck between us, you
        know.

                    LONGWORTH
        That wasn't my intention.

                    OGLETREE
        I meant between me and Janice.

Longworth studies his partner. The gun he
hasn't shot yet.

                    LONGWORTH
        What happened?

                    OGLETREE
        Everything happened. I mean. I
        lost my confidence. Lost my one
        good thing here at home. Sick and
        tired of hearing me bitch about
        you every night. I don't know.
        Maybe I should've given her kids.
        Got so bad I didn't know where I
        wanted to be. I didn't want to be
        at home, didn't wanna be at work.
        Have you ever not wanted to be
        anywhere?

                    LONGWORTH
        Here. I hate it here. But the golf
        is great - and I think I might
        have met someone. She has a son
        and is married to a guy in prison.
        So we'll have to see how that
        goes.

The two men look at each other. Ogletree
struggling.

> OGLETREE
> Maybe you could give me an hour?

> LONGWORTH
> How's that again?

> OGLETREE
> So I don't have to shoot you.

Longworth looks at Ogletree.

> LONGWORTH
> You wouldn't get very far.

Ogletree starting to agitate. Then realizes why Longworth is being so cavalier.

His backyard has quietly been crept up on by DOZENS of Kevlar-suited, Highway Patrol Personnel. Guns trained on him.

A long beat. Ogletree's shoulders slump slightly.

EXT. BELLEAIR COUNTRY CLUB - FAIRWAY - DAY

CLOSE on a Titleist, sitting up in the fairway as we WIDEN to find Carlos balling up the now-stripped away Crime Scene Tape.

Longworth pulls a club, sets up to strike his ball.

> CARLOS
> Did he say why?

> LONGWORTH
> Not really. He blamed me.

> CARLOS
> I can see him doing that.

> LONGWORTH
> Right. I'm so hard to work with a
> man killed his wife.

> CARLOS
> You are.

Longworth strikes the ball, nice and crisp.
They watch it land softly on the green
about a hundred and forty yards away.

> LONGWORTH
> See that? Over your rudeness, and
> I still punch it up there.

EXT. BELLEAIR COUNTRY CLUB - VARIOUS - DAY

Various shots, as Longworth splits fairways
and drops putts on his quest to break
eighty. Sequence ends with his approach
shot on eighteen landing thirty feet short
of the hole.

EXT. BELLEAIR COUNTRY CLUB - EIGHTEENTH
GREEN - DAY

Longworth makes a show of repairing ball
marks.

> CARLOS
> Those aren't even yours.

> LONGWORTH
> They're in my line.

> CARLOS
> Only if you hit the sweetest shot
> of your entire life.

Longworth jogs back to his ball, takes a
couple of practice swings, addresses and

then hits it, blading it a little.

The ball rolls twelve feet past the cup.

EXT. BELLEAIR COUNTRY CLUB - EIGHTEENTH
GREEN - DAY

Longworth stalks his twelve-foot putt,
checking it from every angle, kneeling,
squinting. Then gets over his putt.

> LONGWORTH
> If I make this and break eighty.
> You're not going to kill your wife
> are you?

> CARLOS
> And give you the satisfaction of
> arresting me?

He takes a couple of smooth, sweeping
practice putts. Sets up, eyes his line,
then pulls back and strokes the ball.

It singes the cup on the outside, rolls
past four feet.

> CARLOS
> Yeah, baby.

> LONGWORTH
> Are you kidding me? I miss and
> you're happy? You're an asshole.

> CARLOS
> Why am I an asshole?

> LONGWORTH
> I wouldn't be like Yeah baby if you
> blew a chance to break eighty...

Longworth goes to pick up his ball.

                    CARLOS
          Whoa, whoa. What are you doing?

                    LONGWORTH
          You're not gonna give me that?

                    CARLOS
          It's four feet.

                    LONGWORTH
          You won't give me that for eighty?

                    CARLOS
          Not four feet.

                    LONGWORTH
          Are you an asshole now?

He putts the ball. But before it hits the
hole --

                    CALLIE (V.O.)
          An eighty-one?

EXT. ROBBIE'S RAW BAR - DAY

Callie with Longworth, at the bar, sipping
longnecks.

                    CALLIE
          You three putted the last hole?

                    LONGWORTH
          Burned the edge on the outside,
          rolled five feet past. He gave me
          that one.

                    CALLIE
          A gimmie eighty-one. Wow.

                    LONGWORTH
I feel okay about it. My game is
in good shape, left a few shots
out there, but that's golf. I feel
okay.

                    CALLIE
You watch too much Golf Channel.

Longworth noticing a guy at a booth
checking Callie out.

                    CALLIE
Thanks for taking Jeff fishing.

                    LONGWORTH

Sure.

                    CALLIE
His father never did anything like
that.

                    LONGWORTH
Well he was trying to put a roof
over his family's head. You know,
by stealing things that didn't
belong to him.

                    CALLIE
I'm not making excuses. I knew
what he was doing. I didn't like
it, and I told him so. But I knew
what he was doing.

                    LONGWORTH
You could have left him.

                    CALLIE
I could have. But I didn't. Then I
didn't have to.

                    LONGWORTH
          You wouldn't be the first woman to
          divorce a man in prison.

                    CALLIE
          Yeah, but then I'm the woman who
          divorced her husband in prison.

She looks at him to see if he gets that.

                    CALLIE
          There was good in Ray once. Maybe
          this is bottom for him.

                    LONGWORTH
          Odds are not in favor of that
          being the case.

                    CALLIE
          Odds don't get any better if I
          divorce him.

Which puts her in a difficult place. A point
he considers.

                    LONGWORTH
          I should go.

                    CALLIE
          I thought he was meeting you here.

                    LONGWORTH
          The lucky candidate? He got here
          about twenty minutes ago.

Callie confused - then figures out what he
did when she looks to see the guy in the
booth who's been checking her out.

                    CALLIE
          You'll never find a partner that way.

> LONGWORTH
> Not a good one.

As he rises to leave...

> CALLIE
> I don't get Jeff back from his
> Grandma's until morning. How 'bout
> that first date we never had?

They look at each other. A beat that
quickly fills with promise.

> LONGWORTH
> Give me an hour to see what this
> joker has to offer?

She glances at the guy - who remarkably is
still checking her out.

> CALLIE
> An hour is generous.

Longworth throws some bills down and
we FOLLOW him to the booth, where he
introduces himself.

> LONGWORTH
> Randy Cromwell?

> CROMWELL
> Yeah?

> LONGWORTH
> Jim Longworth.

The guy looks at Longworth, knows now he
was checking out his lady friend.

> CROMWELL
> Jim. Nice to meet you.

> LONGWORTH
> Thanks for driving up.

> CROMWELL
> Yeah, I got here a little
> early...

> LONGWORTH
> Yeah, I noticed that.

Longworth slides in on the other side.
Cromwell knows he's already screwed.

> LONGWORTH
> So you want to be my partner?

FADE OUT.

THE END...

...THE SCRIPT IS ONLY THE BEGINNING.

New Original Drama Series

SUN 10/9C | JULY 11